Garfield
What's Cooking?

Selected cartoons by
JiM DAViS

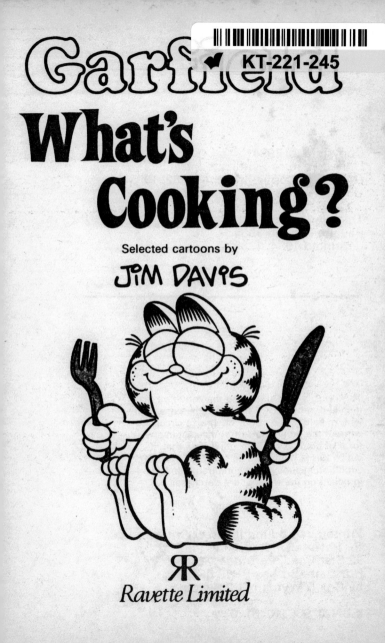

RR
Ravette Limited

This edition first published by
Ravette Limited 1984
Reprinted 1984, 1985

Printed and bound in Great Britain
for Ravette Limited,
12 Star Road, Partridge Green,
Horsham, Sussex RH13 8RA
by Cox & Wyman Ltd, Reading

ISBN 0 906710 51 0

© 1983 United Feature Syndicate, Inc.

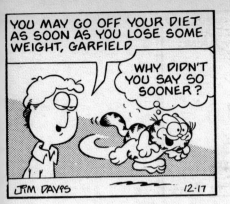

© 1982 United Feature Syndicate, Inc.

© 1982 United Feature Syndicate, Inc.

© 1982 United Feature Syndicate, Inc.

© 1982 United Feature Syndicate, Inc.

© 1983 United Feature Syndicate, Inc.

© 1983 United Feature Syndicate, Inc.

© 1983 United Feature Syndicate, Inc.

© 1983 United Feature Syndicate, Inc.

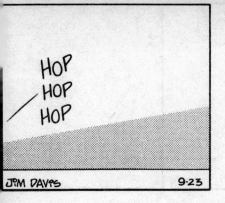

JIM DAVIS 9-23

© 1983 United Feature Syndicate, Inc.

© 1983 United Feature Syndicate, Inc.

© 1983 United Feature Syndicate, Inc.

© 1983 United Feature Syndicate, Inc.

© 1983 United Feature Syndicate, Inc.

7-29

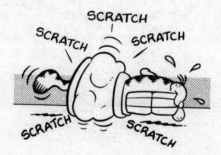

© 1983 United Feature Syndicate, Inc.

3-10

THERE IS ONE
THING I LIKE
ABOUT THIS
SWEATER

Z

© 1983 United Feature Syndicate, Inc.

1-28

© 1983 United Feature Syndicate, Inc.

© 1983 United Feature Syndicate, Inc.

GEE...UH, THANKS, ODIE

CLUNK!

WHAT IS IT, GARFIELD?

I'D WAGER IT WOULD HAVE BEEN EASIER TO RECOGNIZE BEFORE IT WANDERED INTO TRAFFIC

JIM DAVIS   7-26

© 1983 United Feature Syndicate, Inc.

© 1983 United Feature Syndicate, Inc.

© 1983 United Feature Syndicate, Inc.

EEEEEEK!

JIM DAVIS

1-31

I'M ALMOST AFRAID TO ASK WHAT HAPPENED HERE

© 1983 United Feature Syndicate, Inc.

© 1983 United Feature Syndicate, Inc.

I SEWED POOKY'S ARM BACK ON AS GOOD AS NEW, GARFIELD

YES, BUT WILL HE EVER PLAY THE PIANO AGAIN?

ME THINKS THE CAT DOTH EXPECT TOO MUCH

© 1983 United Feature Syndicate, Inc.

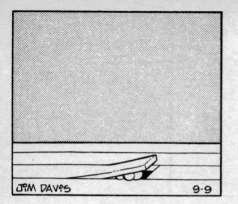

I'M BORED. I NEED TO ADD SOME SPARKLE TO MY LIFE

© 1982 United Feature Syndicate, inc.

© 1983 United Feature Syndicate, Inc.

5-5   © 1983 United Feature Syndicate, Inc.

© 1983 United Feature Syndicate, Inc.

JIM DAVIS   6-7

THINK ABOUT A BIG, JUICY BONE, ODIE

© 1983 United Feature Syndicate, Inc.

© 1983 United Feature Syndicate, Inc.

© 1983 United Feature Syndicate. Inc.

© 1983 United Feature Syndicate, Inc.

© 1983 United Feature Syndicate, Inc.   JiM DAViS

OTHER GARFIELD BOOKS IN THIS SERIES